Cookie Monster's CIRCLE BOOK

lyrics by *Jeffrey Moss*
words & pictures by *Mike Smollin*

featuring Jim Henson's Muppets
On Sesame Street, Cookie Monster is performed by **FRANK OZ**
and Herry Monster by **JERRY NELSON.**

A SESAME STREET BOOK

Published by Western Publishing Company, Inc.
in conjunction with Children's Television Workshop.
© 1972 Children's Television Workshop.

Muppet characters © 1971, 1972 Muppets, Inc.
Based on the song "CIRCLES" © 1970 Festival Attractions, Inc.
(ASCAP) music and lyrics by Jeffrey Moss.
All rights reserved. Produced in U.S.A.

These beautiful tambourines are circles, too. They were given to me by my dear maternal grandmother, and we've got to get out of here before Cookie eats them!
HEY, Cookie Monster, it's time to go home!